TRIP TO TULUM

TRIP TO TULUM
ISBN 0-87416-123-1
A graphic novel illustrated by
Milo Manara
From a script by
Federico Fellini
for a film idea

Edited by Vincenzo Mollica
Colors by Cettina Novelli

With essays by
Federico Fellini
Milo Manara
Vincenzo Mollica
Oreste del Buono
and additional drawings by
Federico Fellini
Milo Manara

Translated by
Stefano Gaudiano (story)
Elizabeth Bell (essays)
Edited by Bernd Metz

First Catalan Communications Edition
November 1990
10 9 8 7 6 5 4 3 2 1

Printed in Catalonia (Spain)

Dep. L.B. 39.197/90

CONTENTS

catalan communications
new york

TRIP TO TULUM

Milo Manara
from a script

Federico Fellini
for a film idea

Vincenzo Mollica, Editor
E. Bell & S. Gaudiano, Translators

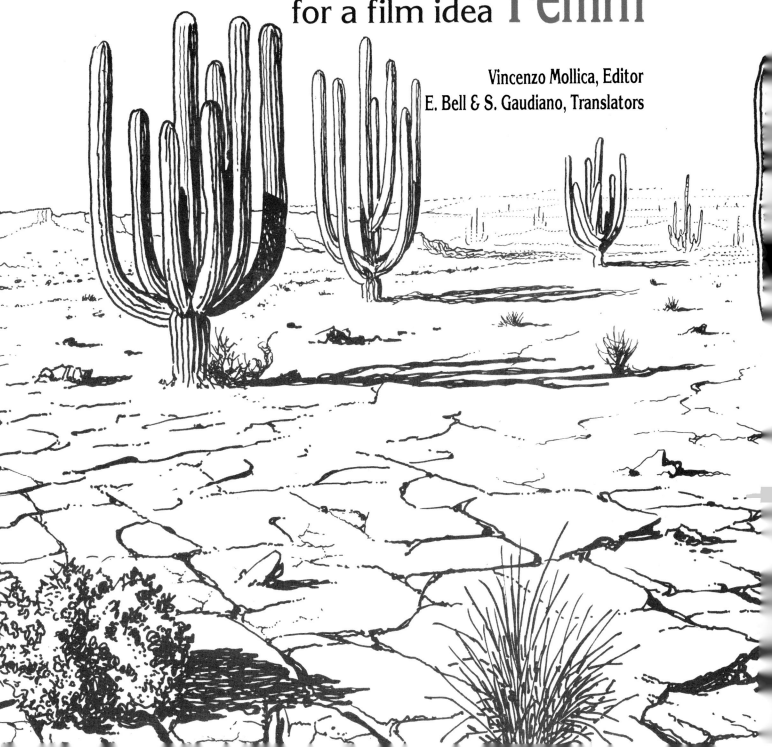

IT WAS LIKE ONE OF THOSE COUNTLESS DREAMS...

"Comics and the ghostly fascination of those paper people, paralyzed in time, marionettes without strings, unmoving, cannot be transposed to film, whose allure is motion, rhythm, dynamic. It is a radically different means of addressing the eye, a separate mode of expression. The world of comics may, in its generosity, lend scripts, characters and stories to the movies, but not its inexpressible secret power of suggestion that resides in that fixity, that immobility of a butterfly on a pin."

Federico Fellini

At first it was like one of those many dreams you keep in a drawer and pull out when your imagination is stirred to revive the dialogue with the impossible. Fellini's affinity for comics is common knowledge, but never until now—except in his youth—has the maestro from Rimini lent one of his subjects to an artist for a graphic novel. It all began in 1986 when *Corriere della Sera* serialized *Trip to Tulum* with the caption, "For the first time, the great director reveals the plot of his next film." Of course, it wasn't Fellini's next film; in fact, he concluded the sixth and last episode with the comment, "I don't know whether I will transfer this narrative to the form of images, or when. But the fact that I accepted the invitation to publish the story before making the film makes me suspect that I was following an unconscious instinct to put it in abeyance. The same instinct tells me that you patient readers who have followed this story to the end should be let in on a little secret: the journey and mysterious adventure that led to this tale, freely retold as cinematic narrative, really happened."

Fellini expressed the desire to have the newspaper story include some illustrations by Manara, who had, a short time earlier, dedicated to Fellini a charming homage, "Untitled" (also published in *Shorts;* New York: Catalan Communications, 1989). Manara has expressed his affection for Fellini's work more than once with visual quotations in his stories, and it's no coincidence that he created the images for advertising *Intervista* and *The Voice of the Moon.* What followed was a dream come true: Manara asked Fellini if he could make a graphic novel out of *Trip to Tulum* and Fellini agreed. It is often overlooked that Fellini's artistic career had early links to caricature and comics: Fellini does excellent

drawings, an aspect of his art that the director in him prefers to minimize. He'll scold me again for bringing it up.

When Fellini set out from Rimini in the late thirties on the adventure that would eventually land him permanently in Rome, the first step along the way was Florence, where he worked for the publisher Nerbini on (among others) two publications: the satirical weekly *420* and *l'Avventuroso*. During the era when fascism decreed rigid isolation, it was forbidden to import American comics, but certain characters from them were continued in adventures created by Italian artists. Legend has it that Fellini wrote several scripts for *Flash Gordon*, illustrated by the exceptional Giove Toppi. Fellini can only recall one title, *Rebo, King of the Mercurians*.

Trip to Tulum ends at the start of a new journey which augurs well for all. Little is left of Fellini's original screenplay. What began with an amused and amicable glance over Manara's shoulder evolved through the episodes into a veritable comics "set," like a film studio. Fellini didn't stick to dialogue and plot; he intervened—especially in the final stages—in decisions about cropping, lighting and the characters' expressions. Manara rose to the occasion with brilliance, adeptness and humility. The result is in your hands. Allow me a word of advice: read it the first time all the way through in the comics tradition, then go back and view each panel as a fragment of a huge fresco. There is the art of drawing, the art of invention, but also the art of looking, one we should cultivate to commune with the muse of the imagination.

You won't see "End" on the last page. Fellini's never used it in a film. He told me why, one day: "I've rejected the word 'End' from the outset. Maybe because when I went to the movies as a kid, I always experienced it as a letdown and an annoyance: The party's over; you have to go now; back to your homework… Beyond that, the word 'End' seems to me like an aggression against the characters one has taken such trouble to make believable, as alive as possible—their lives continue behind the author's back." To which I'd add that I hope the absence of "End" in *Trip to Tulum* also implies that Fellini will decide to extend his venture into the realm of comics. Through some unknown means I became the first to read *Trip to Tulum*, a fantastic journey for all readers of good will who'd like to make a spirited, imaginative stand against the reigning decadence of our times.

Vincenzo Mollica

UNTITLED

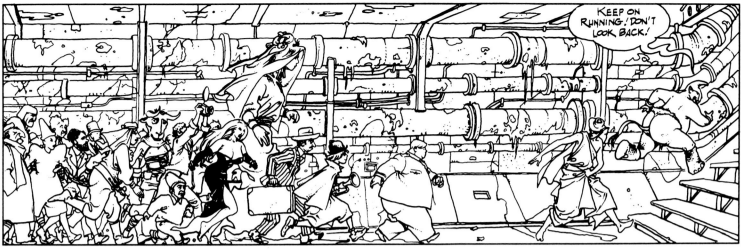

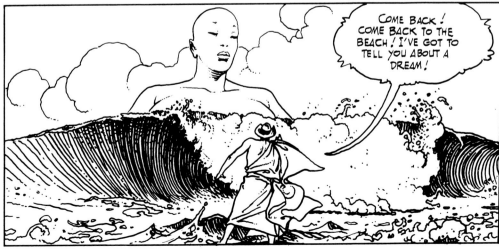

ENDLESS

MEMORY PLAY

I was working my way through an endless sea of papers, *Memoirs,* an arid list of quantifiable facts gathered with statistical rigor, a meticulous, niggling, maddening inventory, without even the grace to lie, and my sense of depression and discouragement was nuanced only by irritation, alienation, boredom and distaste. This revolt, this nausea, suggested the direction for a film. It came to me to tell the story of a man never born, the adventures of a zombie, a macabre marionette without ideas, feelings or opinions of his own, an "Italian," prisoner in his mother's womb, the crypt where he dreams life without living it, in a world exempt from emotions, inhabited solely by shapes: icy, hypnotic vanishing perspectives. These empty volumes form and disintegrate in an aquarium-like enchantment, marine depths lost to memory, where everything flattens, an unknown realm devoid of the merest human landmark.

An abstract, unstructured film on "non-life." No characters, no situations, no beginning, no development, no catharsis, a pointless, frenetic mechanical ballet performed by a clockwork wax museum—Casanova—Pinocchio. I clung desperately to this "nausea of the void," my only foothold for the recounting of Casanova's nonexistent life. This glassy eye, shot through and annihilated by a reality it never judges or interprets through emotions, became the symbol, for me, of the pervading dramatic inertia we let ourselves live with in these times.

Federico Fellini

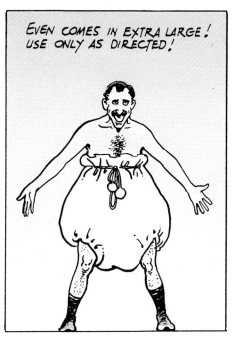

17

TIDY-POOPS

NEVER HAS MAN SO POORLY PLACED HIS TRUST.

IN FACT, THIS NOBLEMAN IS RIGHT! WE CAN'T WRECK HIS LIFE LIKE THIS. WHY NOT STICK ADS ALL OVER THE MONA LISA, IF YOU THINK ABOUT IT... SOME THINGS SHOULD BE RESPECTED!

I TOLD YOU TO SHUT YOUR TRAP, CUNT!

IN ALL MY LIFE I HAVE NEVER WITNESSED SUCH A SCANDAL! I CANNOT BEAR FOR IT TO TAKE PLACE BEFORE MY EYES! EVEN IF MY DUTIES AS HOLDER OF THIS OFFICE DO NOT PERMIT ME TO CALL UPON MY SWORD. AWAY WITH YOU, BOORS! RETURN TO YOUR GUTTER!

HIM AGAIN!

HURRY, MADAM, LET US FLEE! FOLLOW ME!

20

IN A SIMPLE CONVENIENT PACKAGE...

TIDY-POOPS

AND... NO ONE WILL KNOW...

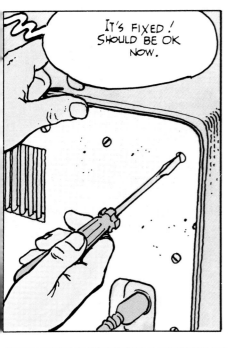

END

23

drawing by F. Fellini

LIGHTNESS

Intervista announced its independence from me quite clearly at the outset, its vital need not to have any of the usual practiced tutors, assistants or experts around it. "I don't need anyone, and besides, you'd be no help, since what I want to do has no relation to what has to be done to make a movie. Everyone out of the ring! Especially Fellini. I'll make myself alone. We can get together at the screening, if you feel like coming. Best to you, and good luck to my unconscious!" Nearly every day the film seemed to speak to me in this tone. All I could do was follow it along its unpredictable trajectory, bolstered by the generosity, confidence and enthusiasm of a cast the greatest circus in the world would envy, the kind that produces sensational spectacle just setting up and dismantling the big top. The film's much like that: a work brought into being with the lightness and skill of the juggler.

Federico Fellini

drawing by F. Fellini

SNAPORAZ, MY COHORT

Marcello Mastroianni is a cohort of mine. Between us there's a rapport without pretensions, a true friendship grounded in a reciprocal distrust of the obligations, duties and rhetoric of friendship. Friendship with him is nothing weighty or moral: it's a way of existing together, of encountering one another, participating in the same jokes, imbroglios and lies… He is a true actor. Psychologically, he approaches his craft in the ideal manner for me, one based on trust: a flexible, intelligent, feminine availability to the character and the author's vision of him.

We chat a bit before each film, enough to know we're on a new journey together. I tell him all I know, at times not much. Marcello doesn't ask any uncomfortable questions; he arrives on the set with a spectator's curiosity, an aura of permanent virginity, and gives the author the provocative sensation that the character doesn't know what's going to happen to him in the next scene. He has a phenomenal instinct for putting everything in its proper place. Far more talented than he guesses, he has a modesty that shields him from the pitfalls awaiting all actors: vanity, excessive exuberance, narcissism, self-aggrandizement, etc…

Marcello Mastroianni isn't me; he's my cinematic double, my alter ego. Giulietta Massina is another alter ego, so is Anita Ekberg; all the characters I direct are alter egos, down to the rhinoceros in *And the Ship Sails On*. If Marcello wears my hat, it's not to identify him as me but to toss out a pointer, a hint, a suggestion, to create a fluid transmission of thought, to enable the simulacrum… I push him to resemble me because it's my most direct means of envisioning the character and his story—a delicate operation made possible only by deep friendship and the shameless desire to put oneself on display.

Federico Fellini

Only true realism
is visionary.

Federico Fellini

LA VOCE
DELLA LUNA

Curiosity is what gets
me up in the morning.
Federico Fellini

drawing by F. Fellini

ONE DAY, MILO...

One day, Milo Manara, blushing with excitement, asked me if I would mind if he made a graphic novel out of *Trip to Tulum,* which he'd read in *Corriere della Sera.* Surprised, perplexed and rather flattered, I didn't quite see how an artist whose imagination was fueled by a joyous eroticism, with his supple, seductive drawing style, could come to terms with situations, characters and anecdotes—a whole style of adventure, really—I found far removed from the rhythms and pacing of comics. I had structured the narrative as a movie and published it in installments in a Milan daily newspaper; it was an attempt to reconstruct my adventures in Mexico seeking Carlos Castañeda, whose work fascinated and disturbed me with each new book. I imagined having him as my guide and companion, retracing the extraordinary initiation journey he made while researching his college thesis on psychotropic plants. As I recount in the narrative, things went quite differently, and I gave up on the idea of a film. To cut myself off from temptation or second thoughts, I accepted the newspaper's offer to publish it as a serialized prose piece. I thought this would be the perfect way to eradicate any lingering urges toward filmmaking, since when I'd first returned from Rome, I'd briefly envisioned the movie I could have put together out of the fragments and scattered recollections preserved in my notebooks: settings, characters, snatches of dialogue.

I found the story fascinating and beautiful because it was quite undecipherable: this film was unlike any other. I told it to Tullio Pinelli,

who helped adapt it for the screen. Milo kept after me with his sweet smile, his radiant blue eyes, his cherub's bangs. All he needed was a gilded trumpet. After I'd done all I could think of to deter him, I gave in. Not out of curiosity—I was already familiar enough with Manara's talent to know that the drawings would be beautiful; his illustrations accompanying the episodes in *Corriere della Sera* were proof of that—but perhaps with the notion that seeing the story transformed into a graphic novel would vanquish once and for all any minute remainder of my impetus to make it a film. I don't know why I still wanted to subtitle it "From a Script for a Film Idea." That's how it all began. Vincenzo Mollica,

Manara's illustrations for the serialized version of *Trip to Tulum* in *Corriere della Sera*, 1986

a reassuring presence, invited me to come in on this unheard-of endeavor. Although Milo had already drawn the first episode, I suggested a different beginning. "Why not start the story at Cinecittà? We'll show Vincenzo coming to interview me and bringing along a beautiful girl."

I had more trouble convincing him to replace the character of the director, myself, with Marcello Mastroianni. I'd noticed on the initial boards that he'd drawn me as very handsome, and although I was flattered, I could already hear my colleagues' snickers on seeing me depicted as vigorous, with a full head of hair. I imagined what my barber would say; he is a fanatic comics reader who tends to flare up in our impassioned debates over the latest publications. "If you'd rather, I can take some more hair off you," Milo said, to which I replied, "And what about when I'm swimming naked in the Yucatan Sea?... Listen, Mastroianni's been appropriated as my alter ego; he's played me in all those movies like *City of Women*. Let's call him Snaporaz, it's a great name for a character in a graphic novel. With him there'll be no problem; with me, there'd be 400 frames where your pen would hesitate to draw me the way I am." My dear Milo gave up on making me handsomer than Robert Taylor or Gregory Peck and accepted my solution: Snaporaz, my alter ego whom I charge to play the director, sets off on an extraordinary, mysterious adventure in the unsettling world of Mexican sorcerors. Caught up in the workings of a new screenplay for a different film, we made notes with Vincenzo Mollica, week after week, for the adventures of a small band of intrepid, though unaware, explorers, changing characters in the new version. Manara drew feverishly, but wasn't exactly punctual when it came to deadlines. Thus I learned with admiration the tremendous technical organization and efficiency required to bring a graphic novel to the bookstore. Just as in filmmaking, you belong to a caste: there are designers, scriptwriters, colorists, letterists who fill the balloons with their clean graphic lines. Artists and artisans take something imaginary and make it concrete for the enjoyment and fascination of millions of readers of all ages, with the same conviction filmmakers bring to the cinema. I think the comic strip was born slightly ahead of the movies. Charlie Chaplin, Buster Keaton, Harry Langdon, Larry Semon (and Ridolini, do you old-timers remember him?), the great comedians of silent film, owe a lot to Happy Hooligan, Felix the Cat, Capitan Cocorico. In countless films, Spielberg, Lucas and I do homage to Winsor McCay's *Little Nemo*, to the hallucinatory astral world of Moëbius, the white-hot brilliance of his colleagues at *Métal Hurlant*. Excuse me if I bring up *Amarcord* again: I constructed and recounted it after the sober frames of the legendary American comic strips of the thirties. *City of Women* pays homage as well, having a character named Snaporaz and his double, Katzone, in affection and gratitude for Panciolini, Cagnara, Archibaldo and Petronilla. And as I ticked off the sequences of *Trip to Tulum* with Milo, and phoned Cettina Novelli to color the boards, and production coordinator Fulvia Serra to make excuses for late deliveries, I found myself in my habitual ambiance, just like the Cinecittà studios, with the same glitches and stumbling blocks, last-minute shifts in direc-

tion, the need to pull it all off, the pleasure
and joy of a marvelous journey into adventure, narrative, invention.

In short, we had a ball; too bad it's over.
But I still have quite a few projects I've treas-
ured for years but left on the back burner, stories and characters that have been keeping me
company, nestled quietly in their box labeled
"Future Script Ideas." For example, there's
a story twice as good as *Trip to Tulum:* it goes
like this...

Federico Fellini
as told to Vincenzo Mollica
February 1990

drawing by F. Fellini

STORYBOARD

sketches by F. Fellini

and drawings by M. Manara

THE THIRD EYE

Fellini is often referred to as *visionary,* but I find the term inaccurate and reductionist. For me, he's vaguely hallucinatory, seeing things that aren't there, caught up in the mirages of an imagination hovering between dream and a state of waking.

I find the word *transfiguration* a more precise association with Fellini. He doesn't see or ask us to see monsters where there are windmills, but through him, the windmill becomes *transfigured,* unveiling to our eyes its essence as the Great Windmill. Out of all the filmmakers in the world, Fellini is the only one who uses the camera as simply what it is: a third eye, the eye of enlightenment. Other directors, in wonderful films, tell us amazing, exciting, tragic, funny stories, but cinema is something else for Fellini. He simply opens the third eye, helping along the *transfiguration* of the universe, and we participate through him.

I've always seen Fellini as a sort of Prometheus, stealing fire from the gods to bring back to man, the artist who endows humanity with a third eye. A sort of religion. Plot, development, narrative thrills and chills have only relative importance for Fellini. What matters to him is the revelation of marvels, the awe-inspiring bringing to light of secret essences, the ineffable universal *transfiguration* uniting everything: humans, animals, plants, objects in a glorious procession of animism, its gentleness, mutual worship, panic.

But this idea of using plot as a mere pretext made it difficult for me as an artist to take on *Trip to Tulum.* Become that third eye? Unthinkable. And I had to avoid merely mimicking Fellini's modus operandi in drawings. I recognized at once the insurmountable barriers to the undertaking, but Fellini himself had already figured out a way around them. From the earliest sketches on, I was breathless, witness to a delicate alchemy. Fellini gently infused his spirit, breathing it in from images to dialogue, from dialogue to action. Little by little, my difficulties burned off like fog. The script went from a simple pretext to images, body—it was *transfigured.* All I had to do was to keep drawing the way I always had. The engine gave a few coughs, and the airplane which had seemed immobilized beneath tons of mud and water began to vibrate, to lift. When the tale was done, the engine was purring and we were flying joyously to the moon.

Milo Manara

WE'D BE THERE ALREADY IF WE'D TAKEN THE SUBWAY!

BUT THE BLUE TROLLEY IS PART OF THE LEGEND...

SURE, BUT IT DOESN'T EXIST ANYMORE!

NOR DOES THE CONDUCTOR, IT SEEMS.

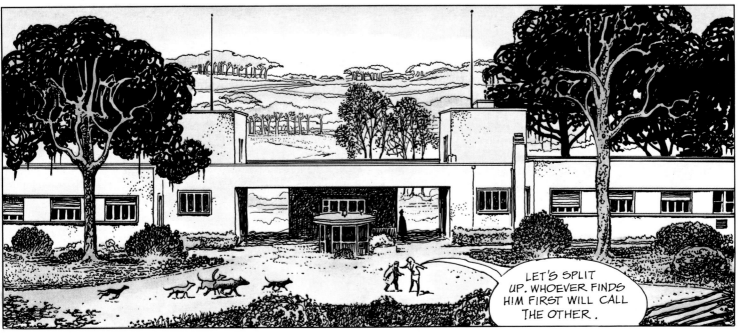

THEY'LL NEVER BELIEVE THIS IN THE NEWSROOM..

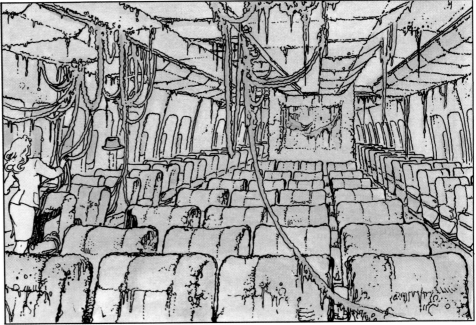

60

VINCENZONE!

VINCENZO IS A JOURNALIST AND HE'LL JOIN YOU ON THIS FANTASTIC TRIP.

WHAT ABOUT ME? CAN'T I HAVE A PART IN THE STORY?

MAYBE LATER ON... BECAUSE I REALLY DON'T KNOW HOW THE STORY WILL TURN OUT.

DO YOU KNOW HOW IT BEGINS, AT LEAST?

YES, THE 747 WILL FLY SNAPORAZ AND VINCENZO TO AMERICA...

AND NOW, I BELIEVE THAT THIS PROJECT, PERHAPS THANKS TO YOU, WILL COME TO LIFE...

ATTENTION PLEASE! DUE TO A COMPUTER MALFUNCTION, THE ELEVATOR WILL BE STOPPED FOR A FEW MINUTES.

SHE'S NOT WELL. MOVE AWAY, LET HER BREATHE!

ELEVATOR SERVICE WILL NOW RESUME. WE APOLOGIZE FOR THE SUDDEN STOP.

ARE YOU ALL RIGHT MA'AM? WE'LL BE THERE IN A FEW SECONDS.

BEFORE I GOT IN, I HAD A FEELING THE ELEVATOR WOULD STOP.

YOU ALREADY KNOW MOST EVERYTHING ABOUT THE MOVIE MY FATHER AND I WILL PRODUCE...

...YOU ALSO KNOW THAT OTHERS HAVE TAKEN A CRACK AT THIS PROJECT!

I WANT TO THANK THE CHILEAN DIRECTOR, JODO-ROWSKY, WHO WAS ON THE VERGE OF ACTUALLY SHOOTING. WE'RE SORRY HE HAD TO STOP, BUT HAPPY WE GOT THE JOB.

I'M DISAPPOINTED, OF COURSE, BUT YOU HAVE MY HEARTFELT BEST WISHES, AND A PIECE OF ADVICE FOR SNAPORAZ, IF I MAY: THE MESSAGES TO READ ARE THOSE NEVER RECEIVED.

I HOPE NINOLA, WHO WAS TO STAR IN MY MOVIE, MIGHT ALSO BE SUITABLE FOR THE NEW PRODUCTION. SHE'S GOT A GREAT DISPOSITION, AND MOREOVER, NO WEATHER REPORT IS AS ACCURATE AS HER PREDICTIONS, WHICH IS A PRICELESS GIFT FOR ANYONE SHOOTING OUTDOORS.

THE TASK MIGHT WELL HAVE BEEN IMPOSSIBLE. THE PHILOSOPHICAL AND RELIGIOUS IDEOLOGY OF THAT STORY REVOLUTIONIZED OUR PROJECTIONS OF OTHER DIMENSIONS, FRUSTRATING ANY ATTEMPT TO TRANSLATE IT INTO CONCEPTS AND IMAGES...

COULD YOU BE CLEARER, MR. MOEBIUS?

WE WANT TO IMAGINE OTHER DIMENSIONS AS PURE LIGHT AND ECSTASY. WE CAN'T ACCEPT THE NOTION THAT THEY MAY IN FACT BE DARKNESS AND COSMIC SOLITUDE

WELL, VERY INTERESTING. WE THANK MOEBIUS, JODOROWSKY, AND EVERYONE HERE AND EVEN THOSE WHO COULDN'T JOIN US.

SPEAKING OF MISSING PEOPLE, THE ANTHROPOLOGIST WHO INITIATED THE WHOLE PROJECT COULDN'T BE WITH US TONIGHT...

WHAT THEY SAY ISN'T VERY ENCOURAGING... WHAT ARE YOU LOOKING AT?

SIBYL, WHERE'RE YOU GOING?

70

THIS FALCON HAS FOLLOWED ME AROUND SINCE WE STARTED WORKING ON THIS FILM.

EVERY MORNING I FIND HIM ON MY WINDOW LEDGE, AND WHEN I GO INTO THE CITY, I LOOK UP... AND THERE HE IS AMONG THE SKY-SCRAPERS, CIRCLING SLOWLY, HIGH IN THE SKY.

IT'S ALWAYS THE SAME ONE, I REC-OGNIZE HIM.

TELEPHONE FOR MR. SNAPORAZ... MR. SNAPORAZ IS WANTED ON THE TELEPHONE...

SNAPORAZ, I FOUND A CRYPTIC MESSAGE FOR YOU ON THE WINDSHIELD.

LISTEN...

SIBYL, JUST WHERE DO YOU THINK YOU'RE GOING?

LET GO!

THAT VOICE ON THE PHONE SAID WE'D NEVER MEET UP WITH THE ANTHROPOLOGIST, BECAUSE HE ABANDONED HIS BODY SOME TIME AGO. HE'S NOT DEAD, BUT HE DOESN'T HAVE A HUMAN FORM...

FASCINATING... THE ANCIENT TOLTEC SAGES KNEW THE ART OF LEAVING THEIR BODY. HANDY, ISN'T IT?

LEMME GO! I HAVE TO FOLLOW MY IMPULSES...I CAN'T CONTROL THEM.

81

83

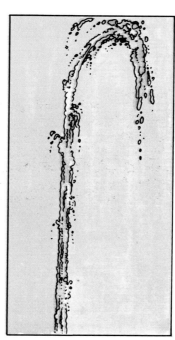

YOU WERE GREAT !
WE DID IT .
HE'S NOT DEAD !
HA ! HA ! HA !

89

HOW CAN YOU TELL THAT IT'S FEMALE?

BY THE RUBY-COLORED PUPILS. THEY CHANGE COLOR AT NIGHT. AM I TALKING TOO MUCH, MY RECKLESS FRIEND?

ON THE DAY OF THE FALCONS, MY MOTHER WOULD ENTERTAIN ME AND MY 26 BROTHERS BY CHANGING HERSELF INTO ONE OF THESE BIRDS.

HERNANDEZ COULD TELL STORIES FOR DAYS INTO NIGHTS. THAT'S ONE OF THE REASONS WHY I DECIDED TO LET HIM GO. TODAY IS THE LAST DAY THAT HE'LL BE WORKING IN THE HOTEL.

I'M VERY GRATEFUL FOR ALL YOU'VE DONE SINCE MY GRANDPARENTS LEFT ME TO MANAGE BABEL TOWER, HERNANDEZ, BUT YOU SHOULDN'T FRIGHTEN THESE DISTINGUISHED GUESTS, WHO HAVE ALREADY BEEN STRAINED BY THE UNUSUAL EVENTS AROUND THEM.

WHY DO AZTEC PYRAMIDS HAVE STAIRS GOING TO THE TOP, UNLIKE THE EGYPTIAN ONES?

FOR THE PEOPLE OF THAT VERY ANCIENT CIVILIZATION...

...IT WAS A SYMBOL FOR THE UNION BETWEEN EARTH AND SKY, TO WHICH EVERYONE ASPIRED AND ALL WERE WELCOMED. THAT'S WHY AZTEC PYRAMIDS HAVE STAIRS...

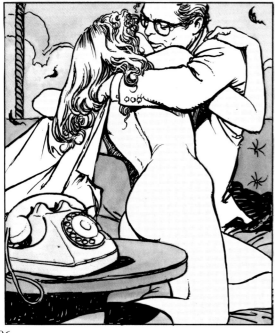

driiiin
driiiin

WHO?... FELLINI?! PUT HIM ON... FEDERICO, OF ALL TIMES FOR YOU TO FINALLY CALL...

WOULD YOU LIKE TO JOIN ME ON A SHORT TRIP? WE'RE GOING TO VISIT EMILIANO. HE'S GONE TO SEE HIS UNCLE...

...A GREAT SORCERER WHO'S VERY ILL. HIS VILLAGE IS IN THE HEART OF THE DWARF JUNGLE, BY THE RUINS OF THE TEMPLE OF THE DESCENDING GOD. IT'S VERY FAR...

...BUT IF WE CAN MAKE OURSELVES AS LIGHT AS THESE KITES, WE COULD GET THERE BEFORE DAWN...

...IT'S VERY EASY, BUT IT COULD ALSO BE VERY DANGEROUS. IT'S A MATTER OF JOINING THE COSMIC SELF WITH THE KITE AND IMAGINING THAT THE KITE'S STRING IS THE SILVER STRAND WHICH CONNECTS THE COSMIC TO THE PHYSICAL SELF.

AS A KID I USED TO ENVY FLASH GORDON AND MANDRAKE SO MUCH... AND NOW I'M FLYING JUST LIKE THEM.

FOR SOMEONE'S WHO'S SO DEMANDING, THIS LADY'S THOUGHTLESSLY LATE. MR. SNAPORAZ, LOOK OUT!

106

THE SORCERER GENNARO, IN HIS IMPRESSIVE LIQUID FORM, SHINING UNDER THE MOONLIGHT, IS TELLING THE FOREIGNER THE SECRET KNOWLEDGE OF THOSE ANCIENT SEERS, THE TOLTECS.

THEY WERE NOT A RACE, THEY WERE NOT A PEOPLE, BUT MEN WHO WERE ABLE TO BRING OUT THE DIVINE WITHIN US. THEY KNEW THE NATURAL LAW THAT CHANGES THE VIBRATIONS OF COSMIC ENERGY...

...BY HOLDING THEM AT THE INFINITE KNOTS WHICH DEFINE THE ELEMENTS SURROUNDING US IN THE UNIVERSE WE CALL LIFE. THEY COULD UNDERSTAND AND COMMUNICATE WITH STONES, PLANTS, AND WITH ALL THE ANIMALS ON EARTH, IN THE AIR AND IN THE WATER.

WHEN THE ARMIES OF THE INVADERS RAPED AND PILLAGED THEIR LANDS...

... SOME OF THE SEERS, IN ORDER TO SAFEGUARD THEIR KNOWLEDGE, DECIDED TO DISPERSE THROUGHOUT THE WORLD...

...AS SO MANY TINY, SPIRITUAL POWER SOURCES, TO INSTILL IN HUMANITY, UNHAPPY AND IGNORANT, A FEELING OF ENDLESS FREEDOM.

BUT MAYBE THE TIME HASN'T COME YET, AND THE "NEW SEERS," KEEPERS OF THAT ANCIENT KNOWLEDGE, LIVE AMONG US, UNKNOWN OR IGNORED.

ANYONE COULD BE LUCKY ENOUGH TO RUN INTO ONE OF THEM, BUT THE WORLD IS TOO OLD TO RECOGNIZE THE NEW WITHIN THE ANCIENT.

HELEN!

HELEN!

WHO CAN SAY?

BUT IF ALL OF THIS DID HAPPEN, SOMEONE MIGHT PASS THE TALE ON AND SOMEONE MIGHT LISTEN...

AND HOW DOES THE STORY END, MR. FELLINI?

END?... ASK, RATHER, WHEN DOES IT BEGIN... WELL, IT BEGINS NOW, LIKE THIS...

LAST INSTALLMENT OR ETERNAL RETURN?

To address the grandiose nature and megalomania of the Magician from Rimini, I must return to the twin sources of the cinema and the comic strip. The official dates speak for themselves: the first movie by the Lumière brothers, *Workers Leaving the Factory,* was shown at the Grand Café in Paris on the 28th of December, 1895, and Richard Felton Outcault's *Yellow Kid,* the first comic strip, was published in the Sunday edition of the *New York World* on July 7th, 1895. Both were forms of narrative told with images, one still, the other in motion; their parallel evolution underscores their differences. They would eventually come together via a later discovery: animation.

Federico Fellini has always been in love with the comic strip. His itinerary from his native Romany to Rome led him through Florence, home of Nerbini, the publisher of *l'Avventuroso.* This was a weekly printed in colors more brilliant than the original strips, which familiarized Italians with the heros of American strips: Alex Raymond's Flash Gordon, Secret Agent X-9, Jungle Jim; Lee Falk and Phil Davis's Mandrake the Magician; Lee Falk and Ray Moore's The Phantom; etc...

When the "Minculpop"[1] outlawed American comic strips in Italy, according to one of the countless Fellinian legends (the Magician from Rimini himself often prefaces things with "according to legend..."), Federico wrote the script for a domestic version of *Flash Gordon,* drawn by the talented Giove Toppi.

In my time, there was even a rumor that after rejection by the Cultural Ministry, Fellini drew the frames himself. In any case, the graphic text is an inescapable element of Fellinian culture. He admires it, follows its development and borrows from it without false scruples.

Trip to Tulum doesn't date from 1938, when comic strips were banned from publications aimed at Italian youth, but from 1965, when Fellini sent producer Dino De Laurentiis a long letter proposing a film project entitled *The Journey of G. Mastorna.* G. for Giuseppe, Giuseppe Mastorna, a cellist who finds himself on an airplane caught in a snowstorm. There is panic on board; the pilot loses control... Then a sudden unearthly calm envelops them and the airplane lands on the square of an unknown city, in the shadow of a large Gothic church. A police van carries the travelers, in shock, to a motel where they are unable to make any phone calls because the lines have been cut. After numerous misunderstandings and disappointments, G. Mastorna discovers he is dead. *The Journey of G. Mastorna,* a sort of voyage beyond the grave, immediately troubled the superstitious De Laurentiis. Subsequent developments bore out his superstitions.

In preparation, the film ran into an impressive array of setbacks, errors, mishaps and various snags, while De Laurentiis increasingly blamed the ill-starred subject material. One day in 1966, just as the finishing touches were being made to the most imposing of the sets, Fellini had a terrifying nightmare: the cathedral of Cologne, which had inspired one of his sets, came crashing down around him, stone by stone, in a matter of seconds. More bad dreams followed, and Fellini at last wrote to De Lauren-

tiis that he didn't want to make *The Journey of G. Mastorna* anymore. The producer demanded 1.1 billion lire in expenses and damages. There were reconciliations, new estrangements, intercessions by foreign and Italian producers. Fellini's *Libro dei Sogni* (Dream Book), containing his drawings and commentary about his dream life, bears vivid witness to this period of anguish, disillusionment and resentment. One day in 1967, Fellini felt extremely ill and was rushed to the Salvator Mundi Clinic. De Laurentiis, skeptical of this sudden indisposition, sent his financial advisors to see Fellini. When they returned with sorrowful expressions and sad news, the Neapolitan producer broke down and sobbed. When Fellini finally returned to public life, another Neapolitan producer, Alberto Grimaldi, who had grown rich on the films of Sergio Leone, asked to become his producer and took care of his past debts. Legend has it that De Laurentiis knelt down and gave thanks to San Gennaro.

Alberto Grimaldi wanted to produce, among other films, *The Journey of G. Mastorna,* but the dangerous project was postponed, perhaps indefinitely, which seemed to contribute to its aura of bad luck. The idea of a great journey into forbidden spheres continues to haunt Fellini. In "Toby Dammit," Fellini's episode of the 1967 film *Spirits of the Dead,* we encounter elements of *The Journey of G. Mastorna:* the airplane lands and Terence Stamp disembarks in the twilit irreality of Fiumicino, into the midst of a crowd that seems to come from another world. *Fellini Satyricon* is the third great journey of this century by a figurative visionary. The first began in 1905 in the *Sunday New York Herald,* where Winsor McCay's comic strip devoted to the dreams of Little Nemo rivaled Sigmund Freud at interpreting the subconscious. In 1934 Alex Raymond inaugurated another great journey in the King Features' Sunday syndication of *Flash Gordon.* The third, Fellini's, takes place in the degenerate Rome of 1969, situated between Little Nemo's Slumberland and Flash Gordon's planet Mongo…

In each new Fellini film there's an allusion to *The Journey of G. Mastorna,* just as in this book which takes the place of another indefinitely postponed film. *The Journey of G. Mastorna* amounts to a stowaway within *Trip to Tulum.* The beautiful blonde, to save the Magician from Rimini's hat from sinking, falls into the pond at Cinecittà and ends up in front of the fateful airplane. It offers, once again, the terrible journey. This time Fellini's mania for changing actors doesn't kick in the way it did in the times of *The Journey of G. Mastorna.* Marcello Mastroianni is inside the submerged airplane and bears the same name as in vulgar kids' games: Snaporaz, the name Fellini gave him for his great ovarian voyage in *City of Women.* With one difference: Milo Manara, an inspired Raphael with roots in erotica, has miraculously restored him to the almost unbearable beauty of his earliest career, when he and Sophia Loren were the most irresistible couple in the world. This graphic novel is a long hoped-for event in Manara's wacky, broad-ranging career as an artist. And Fellini signed on with cordiality and complicity. Beside them, between them, was their eternal intermediary Vincenzo, Big Kind Vincenzo Mollica, without whom *Trip to Tulum* would probably never have arrived at its destination. But then, did it? And if it did, does that mean it's over? Is it still happening? Or is it starting over? Who can say?

And the Ship Sails On has five or six endings; it arrives and starts all over again, like *The Voice of the Moon,* and may not even need to come into port to make a new departure.

Oreste del Buono

[1]The slangy abbreviation of Ministerio de Cultura Populare (Ministry of Popular Culture), "Minculpop" has a humorous phonetic resemblance to the Italian for "mea culpa."

Also Available
by
Milo Manara